Student Practice No

Contents

Lesson notes 2

Student's termly evaluation sheets 40

Practice tips 43

Instrument care 44

Preparing for a concert or an exam 45

Concert/exam day checklist 45

Treble and bass clef note names 46

Circle of fifths 46

Musical words and symbols 47

Notes 48

Teacher's details

Contact number ....

Contact email ....

Lesson day/time ....

Published by
Trinity College London Press Ltd
trinitycollege.com

Registered in England
Company no. 09726123

Printed in England by Halstan & Co, Amersham, Bucks

Date: 26.3.2019

Warm-ups & technical work:

Pieces:

1. Das Veilchen p.1 singing
   The rest : words (pronunciation)
2. Somewhere ! Speak words ridiculously
3. Kea Rewali | Open with hot potatoe mouth.

Improvisation/aural/sight reading/musical knowledge:

Theory: Further at own pace.

Focus for the week/comments:

This week I practised on (circle the days):   M   T   W   Th   F   Sat   Sun

Parent's/carer's comments:

Lesson notes   Date:

Warm-ups & technical work:

Pieces: Das Veilchen : listen to
                 Elly Ameling
                 Elizabeth Schwarzkopf.

            Continue with songs -
            Bring also: Argentina.

Improvisation/aural/sight reading/musical knowledge:

Theory: Further as it suits you
              (plus missed out bits!) lol

Focus for the week/comments:

This week I practised on (circle the days):   M   T   W   Th   F   Sat   Sun

Parent's/carer's comments:

3

Lesson notes

Date:

Warm-ups & technical work:

Pieces:

Improvisation/aural/sight reading/musical knowledge:

Theory:

Focus for the week/comments:

This week I practised on (circle the days): **M   T   W   Th   F   Sat   Sun**

Parent's/carer's comments:

4

Date:

Warm-ups & technical work:

Pieces:

Improvisation/aural/sight reading/musical knowledge:

Theory:

Focus for the week/comments:

This week I practised on (circle the days): M   T   W   Th   F   Sat   Sun

Parent's/carer's comments:

Date:

Warm-ups & technical work:

Pieces:

Improvisation/aural/sight reading/musical knowledge:

Theory:

Focus for the week/comments:

This week I practised on (circle the days): **M   T   W   Th   F   Sat   Sun**

Parent's/carer's comments:

Date:

Warm-ups & technical work:

Pieces:

Improvisation/aural/sight reading/musical knowledge:

Theory:

Focus for the week/comments:

This week I practised on (circle the days): M   T   W   Th   F   Sat   Sun

Parent's/carer's comments:

Date:

Warm-ups & technical work:

Pieces:

Improvisation/aural/sight reading/musical knowledge:

Theory:

Focus for the week/comments:

This week I practised on (circle the days): M   T   W   Th   F   Sat   Sun

Parent's/carer's comments:

Date:

Warm-ups & technical work:

Pieces:

Improvisation/aural/sight reading/musical knowledge:

Theory:

Focus for the week/comments:

This week I practised on (circle the days): M   T   W   Th   F   Sat   Sun

Parent's/carer's comments:

Date:

Warm-ups & technical work:

Pieces:

Improvisation/aural/sight reading/musical knowledge:

Theory:

Focus for the week/comments:

This week I practised on (circle the days): M   T   W   Th   F   Sat   Sun

Parent's/carer's comments:

Date:

Warm-ups & technical work:

Pieces:

Improvisation/aural/sight reading/musical knowledge:

Theory:

Focus for the week/comments:

This week I practised on (circle the days): M   T   W   Th   F   Sat   Sun

Parent's/carer's comments:

Date:

Warm-ups & technical work:

Pieces:

Improvisation/aural/sight reading/musical knowledge:

Theory:

Focus for the week/comments:

This week I practised on (circle the days): M   T   W   Th   F   Sat   Sun

Parent's/carer's comments:

Date:

Warm-ups & technical work:

Pieces:

Improvisation/aural/sight reading/musical knowledge:

Theory:

Focus for the week/comments:

This week I practised on (circle the days): M   T   W   Th   F   Sat   Sun

Parent's/carer's comments:

Date:

Warm-ups & technical work:

Pieces:

Improvisation/aural/sight reading/musical knowledge:

Theory:

Focus for the week/comments:

This week I practised on (circle the days): M   T   W   Th   F   Sat   Sun

Parent's/carer's comments:

Date:

Warm-ups & technical work:

Pieces:

Improvisation/aural/sight reading/musical knowledge:

Theory:

Focus for the week/comments:

This week I practised on (circle the days): M   T   W   Th   F   Sat   Sun

Parent's/carer's comments:

Date:

Warm-ups & technical work:

Pieces:

Improvisation/aural/sight reading/musical knowledge:

Theory:

Focus for the week/comments:

This week I practised on (circle the days): M   T   W   Th   F   Sat   Sun

Parent's/carer's comments:

Date:

Warm-ups & technical work:

Pieces:

Improvisation/aural/sight reading/musical knowledge:

Theory:

Focus for the week/comments:

This week I practised on (circle the days):   M   T   W   Th   F   Sat   Sun

Parent's/carer's comments:

Date:

Warm-ups & technical work:

Pieces:

Improvisation/aural/sight reading/musical knowledge:

Theory:

Focus for the week/comments:

This week I practised on (circle the days): **M T W Th F Sat Sun**

Parent's/carer's comments:

Date:

Warm-ups & technical work:

Pieces:

Improvisation/aural/sight reading/musical knowledge:

Theory:

Focus for the week/comments:

This week I practised on (circle the days): M   T   W   Th   F   Sat   Sun

Parent's/carer's comments:

Date:

Warm-ups & technical work:

Pieces:

Improvisation/aural/sight reading/musical knowledge:

Theory:

Focus for the week/comments:

This week I practised on (circle the days): M   T   W   Th   F   Sat   Sun

Parent's/carer's comments:

Date:

Warm-ups & technical work:

Pieces:

Improvisation/aural/sight reading/musical knowledge:

Theory:

Focus for the week/comments:

This week I practised on (circle the days): **M   T   W   Th   F   Sat   Sun**

Parent's/carer's comments:

Date:

Warm-ups & technical work:

Pieces:

Improvisation/aural/sight reading/musical knowledge:

Theory:

Focus for the week/comments:

This week I practised on (circle the days):   M   T   W   Th   F   Sat   Sun

Parent's/carer's comments:

Date:

Warm-ups & technical work:

Pieces:

Improvisation/aural/sight reading/musical knowledge:

Theory:

Focus for the week/comments:

This week I practised on (circle the days):   M   T   W   Th   F   Sat   Sun

Parent's/carer's comments:

Date:

Warm-ups & technical work:

Pieces:

Improvisation/aural/sight reading/musical knowledge:

Theory:

Focus for the week/comments:

This week I practised on (circle the days): M   T   W   Th   F   Sat   Sun

Parent's/carer's comments:

Date:

Warm-ups & technical work:

Pieces:

Improvisation/aural/sight reading/musical knowledge:

Theory:

Focus for the week/comments:

This week I practised on (circle the days): M T W Th F Sat Sun

Parent's/carer's comments:

Date:

Warm-ups & technical work:

Pieces:

Improvisation/aural/sight reading/musical knowledge:

Theory:

Focus for the week/comments:

This week I practised on (circle the days): M   T   W   Th   F   Sat   Sun

Parent's/carer's comments:

Date:

Warm-ups & technical work:

Pieces:

Improvisation/aural/sight reading/musical knowledge:

Theory:

Focus for the week/comments:

This week I practised on (circle the days):   M   T   W   Th   F   Sat   Sun

Parent's/carer's comments:

Date:

Warm-ups & technical work:

Pieces:

Improvisation/aural/sight reading/musical knowledge:

Theory:

Focus for the week/comments:

This week I practised on (circle the days):   M   T   W   Th   F   Sat   Sun

Parent's/carer's comments:

Date:

Warm-ups & technical work:

Pieces:

Improvisation/aural/sight reading/musical knowledge:

Theory:

Focus for the week/comments:

This week I practised on (circle the days): M T W Th F Sat Sun

Parent's/carer's comments:

Date:

Warm-ups & technical work:

Pieces:

Improvisation/aural/sight reading/musical knowledge:

Theory:

Focus for the week/comments:

This week I practised on (circle the days):   M   T   W   Th   F   Sat   Sun

Parent's/carer's comments:

Date:

Warm-ups & technical work:

Pieces:

Improvisation/aural/sight reading/musical knowledge:

Theory:

Focus for the week/comments:

This week I practised on (circle the days): M   T   W   Th   F   Sat   Sun

Parent's/carer's comments:

Date:

Warm-ups & technical work:

Pieces:

Improvisation/aural/sight reading/musical knowledge:

Theory:

Focus for the week/comments:

This week I practised on (circle the days): M T W Th F Sat Sun

Parent's/carer's comments:

Date:

Warm-ups & technical work:

Pieces:

Improvisation/aural/sight reading/musical knowledge:

Theory:

Focus for the week/comments:

This week I practised on (circle the days): **M   T   W   Th   F   Sat   Sun**

Parent's/carer's comments:

Date:

Warm-ups & technical work:

Pieces:

Improvisation/aural/sight reading/musical knowledge:

Theory:

Focus for the week/comments:

This week I practised on (circle the days):   M   T   W   Th   F   Sat   Sun

Parent's/carer's comments:

Date:

Warm-ups & technical work:

Pieces:

Improvisation/aural/sight reading/musical knowledge:

Theory:

Focus for the week/comments:

This week I practised on (circle the days): **M** **T** **W** **Th** **F** **Sat** **Sun**

Parent's/carer's comments:

Date:

Warm-ups & technical work:

Pieces:

Improvisation/aural/sight reading/musical knowledge:

Theory:

Focus for the week/comments:

This week I practised on (circle the days): M   T   W   Th   F   Sat   Sun

Parent's/carer's comments:

Date:

Warm-ups & technical work:

Pieces:

Improvisation/aural/sight reading/musical knowledge:

Theory:

Focus for the week/comments:

This week I practised on (circle the days): **M   T   W   Th   F   Sat   Sun**

Parent's/carer's comments:

Date:

Warm-ups & technical work:

Pieces:

Improvisation/aural/sight reading/musical knowledge:

Theory:

Focus for the week/comments:

This week I practised on (circle the days):   M   T   W   Th   F   Sat   Sun

Parent's/carer's comments:

Date:

Warm-ups & technical work:

Pieces:

Improvisation/aural/sight reading/musical knowledge:

Theory:

Focus for the week/comments:

This week I practised on (circle the days): M   T   W   Th   F   Sat   Sun

Parent's/carer's comments:

Student's termly evaluation sheet – Term 1

I feel that I have done well in:

I have enjoyed:

I have played with other people in:

I have performed in:

I have enjoyed listening to:

My aim for next term is to:

Teacher's termly evaluation – Term 1

Student's termly evaluation sheet – Term 2

I feel that I have done well in:

I have enjoyed:

I have played with other people in:

I have performed in:

I have enjoyed listening to:

My aim for next term is to:

Teacher's termly evaluation – Term 2

Student's termly evaluation sheet – Term 3

I feel that I have done well in:

I have enjoyed:

I have played with other people in:

I have performed in:

I have enjoyed listening to:

My aim for next term is to:

Teacher's termly evaluation – Term 3

Practice tips

- Practise regularly in a place where you can concentrate

- Start with tuning and a warm-up

- Read your teacher's notes to help you focus on what you need to do

- Practise technical pieces in sections; avoid starting at the beginning each time

- Practise fast passages slowly, gradually increasing the speed – make yourself keep going and use a metronome to help you

- Vary the order in which you practise your technical work and pieces; this will help keep your mind fresh

- Practise different scales and arpeggios; try making a scale chart so that you don't forget any of them

- Practise scales and arpeggios using different articulation (staccato, legato etc), dynamics, speeds and direction (try them backwards)

- Record yourself playing your pieces and play the recording back, listening for areas where you need to improve

- Between practice sessions research your pieces (the composer, the historical period, the musical form of your pieces etc)

- It would help to have an understanding of the piano accompaniment (where appropriate)

- Always carry a pencil in your instrument case for marking problem areas or making corrections

Instrument care

- Keep your instrument well away from radiators and direct sunlight

- Keep your instrument in a place where the temperature doesn't vary too much

- Hold your instrument carefully and put it in the case when not in use

- Avoid leaving your instrument on a chair or on the floor

- Keep your instrument clean (ask your teacher for advice)

- Tell your teacher if you notice anything that seems wrong with your instrument

- Ensure you always have spare strings/reeds or other appropriate items

Preparing for a concert or an exam

- Make sure that you know exactly what you have to play or do, and in which order

- Practise your performance from start to finish by asking your teacher to arrange a mock performance or exam

- Practise coming on to an imaginary stage or into the exam room. Take time to tune and remember to focus your mind before you start

- Perform your pieces to an audience other than your teacher

- Check when and where your concert/exam is taking place and allow plenty of time to get there

- Allow time for a warm-up beforehand

Concert/exam day checklist

- Instrument

- Other equipment (footstool etc)

- Music

- Piano accompaniment or CD

- Exam appointment form – make sure that you have filled it out beforehand

- Appropriate clothing that allows you to play your instrument comfortably

Treble and bass clef note names

E G B D F   F A C E

G B D F A   A C E G

Circle of fifths

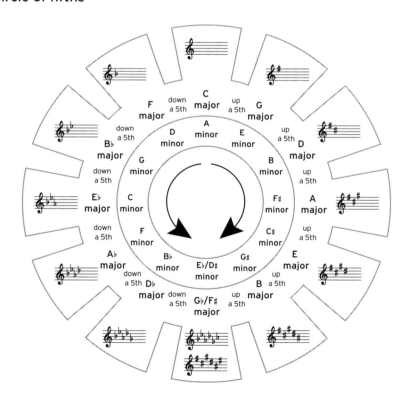

Musical words and symbols

Dynamics

pp (*pianissimo*) – very soft

p (*piano*) – soft

mp (*mezzo piano*) – medium soft

mf (*mezzo forte*) – medium loud

f (*forte*) – loud

ff (*fortissimo*) – very loud

crescendo (*cresc.*) or ◁ – getting gradually louder

decrescendo (*decresc.*) or ▷ – getting gradually softer

diminuendo (*dim.*) or ▷ – getting gradually softer

Tempo marks

Adagio – slow

Andante – at a walking pace

Moderato – at a moderate pace

Allegretto – quite fast but slower than Allegro

Allegro – fast

Vivace – fast and lively

ritenuto (**rit.**) – getting gradually slower

rallentando (**rall.**) – getting gradually slower

accelerando (**accel.**) – getting gradually faster

Notes